Haunted Houses of Harpers Ferry

Haunted Houses

of

Harpers Ferry

Stephen D. Brown

Illustrated by Joseph D. Osmann

The Little Brown House, Harpers Ferry, West Virginia 25425.

SIXTH PRINTING 1981

First published in the United States of America in 1976 by The Little Brown House Publishing Company, Box 179, Harpers Ferry, West Virginia 25425.

Library of Congress Catalog Card Number: 76-398

International Standard Book Number: 0-915782-04-9

For my mother,
who helped make this book possible.

Contents

Introduction

It is said that ghosts and phantom figures roam where the gently rolling hills of Western Maryland and Northern Virginia meet West Virginia's craggy eastern borders at Harpers Ferry. The area is rich in history with Civil War battlegrounds, old homes, and even older legends. It is in this area that these tales of mysterious shadows, ghosts and haunted houses are told . . . .

Haunted Houses of Harpers Ferry is a collection of these stories. After more than two years of research, interviews, and fact-finding, the large number of accounts dealing with ghosts were carefully grouped and selected according to authenticity.

With the possible exception of "Wizard Clip," those stories with heavy religious overtones — such as rites of exorcism to dispell devils or demons — were not included. These may be better suited in a different type of book.

Tales known to be clear fabrications have also been purposefully excluded. The legend of the Snallygaster (from the German *schnellegeister*, meaning quick spirit), falls into this category. The story was reported in major metropolitan newspapers about forty years ago, and even today is well-known. Careful investigation revealed that the huge bird which emitted blood curdling sounds and snatched small children from their mothers was nothing more than an editor's hoax. Ironically similar to Orson Welles' melodrama, "War of the Worlds," the tale soured, and the Snallygaster was quickly drowned in a vat of liquor with the stroke of a pen.

However, the well-known legend of the Snarly Yow, or Black Dog, is included in this book with a very important distinction: credible witnesses saw the dog *recently*. Their experiences appear here in print for the first time, together with the old accounts.

Other recent encounters with ghosts are also reported on these pages for the first time. (The reader should note one story, "The House on High Street," is presented as it was related to the author, and thus appears in the first person form.)

Ghost tales with "political" or "jurisdictional" over-tones have been omitted. Consequently, there are no stories of "border ghosts" — in which "phantoms" move boundary markers between neighboring Maryland and Pennsylvania, or on tracts of disputed land.

The stories presented here have been substantiated usually by more than three living persons, but the actual number of people involved or reporting the story was not set as a deciding criteria. Ghosts have been said to live in many of the older homes in the region, but often the details were too sketchy (or coincidental) to warrant inclusion. Nevertheless, some stories are worth noting:

At Piedmont, one of the Washington homes near Charles Town, West Virginia, a woman was awakened by a mysterious beckoning figure who led her to a second floor room where a portion of the floor had been cut out. Nothing was found under the square.

Sir Edward McPherson, a major during the Mexican War under the command of General Scott, was slain in a duel. His ghost has supposedly haunted Auburn, his ancestral home twelve miles north of Frederick.

Not to be forgotten are the accounts of Screaming Jenny, who caught on fire and for more than one hundred years has been said to run screaming along the ridge of the mountains near Harpers Ferry.

In Thurmont, Maryland, a man was thought to be dead and was buried. The story continues that actually the man was alive, and he frantically clawed at the lid of the coffin until his nails were worn away and fingers bled. It is said that on each anniversary of his death the tombstone turns red, and blood drips from the tombstone onto the ground.

Whether one believes in ghosts, poltergeists or other psychic phenomena, there are mysterious happenings which remain to be explained. Those strange tales which embrace the area around Harpers Ferry — from Thurmont to Frederick to Old South Mountain near Hagerstown, Maryland, to Winchester, Virginia — have been collected to preserve the rich lore that is as much a part of our heritage as the historical events which have shaped our nation.

The Whimpering Child

The cool October nights in Harpers Ferry are often still and quiet, in sharp contrast to the day's bustling visitors and scurrying shopkeepers. At dusk the town is reclaimed by the townspeople, and except for an occasional freight train passing in the night, there is an undisturbed tranquility conducive to sound sleep.

One such evening a man who lived with his children on the top floor of a government building retired to bed, expecting to rise at the usual morning hour. But in the middle of the night he found himself suddenly awake, alert, and acutely aware of strange sounds he had never heard before.

As his eyes grew more sensitive to the glimmering light from the period gaslamps in front of the historic house, he saw nothing unusual in the bedroom; then he heard it again.

It was a muffled sound, a soft whimpering as that of a child. For several moments the man listened to the sounds before it abruptly ceased.

Pulling himself from bed he turned on the room lights, but things were as he had left them. Through the rippled panes of glass he saw only the familiar street scene. Could it have been a dream?

Several nights later he was awakened again. He lay still, listening intently to the muffled cries, the same pitiful whimpering of a small child. The sounds were soft, yet near, as though originating from the very room in which he slept. He got out of bed and tiptoed across the room, trying to get closer to the sounds. In front of the closet he stopped and pressed his ear to the wooden door.

Carefully taking the door handle and securing a firm grip, the man yanked open the door with an explosive energy to expose whatever was inside.

There was nothing. The room was silent. He turned on the light and inspected the closet, but the clothing and shoes were exactly as he had put them. He returned to bed feeling uneasy, sure he had heard *something*.

The strange whimpering sounds were heard a number of times in the ensuing months, but the source could never be located.

One evening after a late dinner the gentleman invited his children to the movies. Gathering themselves up hurriedly, they left the dishes in the sink to be washed later. They went to a local drive-in and returned quite late, about 1:00 A.M. The children were put to bed and the man turned to the dishes in the sink before retiring.

He only had begun his task when the sounds of the whimpering child were heard again. Used to the unusual sounds by now, he casually ordered it to "Be quiet!", but this time the sounds continued. On the third command he turned and peered into his bedroom, *sensing* something. What appeared to be a white cloth ball, about three times the size of a football, flew from the direction of his bedroom closet to his bed. He ran into the bedroom and looked under the bed and under the carpet, but nothing appeared out of the ordinary.

He returned to the kitchen a bit shaken, and hesitatingly picked up another dish to wash. It was then he heard a tremendous *crash*, as though a brick had fallen. He rushed toward the direction of the sound — his bedroom — but again nothing was out of place. The closet was checked but that, too, appeared perfectly safe.

The next day he came across the couple that lived one floor below him in the old building. The couple asked the man what he had been doing the night before, as they had been woken at 1:20 A.M. by a loud noise. The man had no explanation for the strange sound. As they all would soon realize, there weren't explanations for *many* of the strange things that happen around Harpers Ferry.

Spook Hill

The Gapland Road outside of the historic district of Burkittsville, Maryland, winds over the hills and through the valleys to the state park dedicated to Civil War correspondents. The area was the scene of vicious battles during the Civil War, and one in particular is worth noting.

For days Union and Confederate forces marched toward Burkittsville in anticipation of a battle that would determine strategic control of a large area. At dusk the day before the expected encounter, only a large hill separated the two armies. Scouts from both sides saw the fires in the opposing camps, and the night before what would assuredly be a deciding battle, there seemed to be a charged atmosphere of anticipation and restlessness.

The commanders of the Confederate forces had no intention of spending a tranquil night before battle. Troops were quietly mobilized to draw the cannons and ammunition to the top of the separating hill, in order that Rebel forces could gain a strategic advantage during the night by being able to fire down on Union soldiers rather than scrambling for control of the hill when morning came. The horses were quieted and the men stealthily began pulling the implements of war toward the ridge. Hopefully they could gain the position before the Union soldiers awakened.

Alert Union scouts noted the unusual activity during the night, however, and immediately reported the Confederate mobilization to their commanders.

No reveille sounded, and no bugle called. But the Union soldiers were awakened, quickly assembled, and armed. Torchless, the Union army ascended the hill and silently took positions. Heavy artillery was left behind. Below, Confederate troops were struggling with the heavy cannons, 'pushing and pulling them up the face of the hill.

Without warning the Union troops charged, firing into the surprised and unprepared Rebel soldiers. Cannons were abandoned and rolled down the hill as soldiers scrambled for cover and ammunition. Relentless Union soldiers pursued, slaughtering thousands. Remaining Confederate troops regrouped and hastily retreated as the sun rose on the day the battle was supposed to have taken place.

For more than a century residents of the area have seen campfires materialize on open fields and in wooded areas both adjacent to this battlefield and at various locations on South Mountain. Occasionally several phantom-like soldiers are seen stirring fires, but upon closer examination both fire and figures vanish. There is an eerie, intangible quality to the area on certain nights, but that hill — as well as Cherry Lane near Braddock Heights — is not wholly devoid of more tangible evidence.

Many people have taken their automobiles to the location outside of Burkittsville, where the road ascends the hill described. Turning off the ignition and putting the gearshift in neutral, one can sit at the base of the hill . . . then silently begin rolling *up* the hill, powered by unknown means.

It is told phantoms of the Confederate army continue to haunt the area, pushing vehicles up the hill as though they were cannon. No scientific explanation has been offered that satisfies those who know of the haunted hill . . . and the curious phenomena continues to this day.

The House on High Street

as related to the author

We came home one afternoon and found the first sign of a ghost in the house. We had been warned.

It was the little Mexican man, a piece of Aztec pottery dug out of the mountains near Mexico City and brought to the city to be sold on a streetcorner. The statue had an impressive headdress and folded arms, and sat on a deep shelf in the living room, seemingly staring at its observers.

But now, as we entered the room, we saw in the dwindling light the little man shattered into pieces strewn over the carpet. In one corner was the head, separate and quite apart from the appendages found in other locations. It indeed seemed curious at the time, but after the pieces had been gathered, carefully glued together and returned to the shelf, the incident was all but forgotten.

The following week the little Mexican man was again found across the room from where it normally sat, decapitated, as though thrown violently to the floor. Near it were some small volumes and a photograph, its glass casing now cracked; only that morning they had shared a berth with the pottery in the cupboard. The statue was again pieced together and returned to the shelf, but when found a third time inexplicably smashed, it was moved to the piano near the metronome.

The strange sounds began in the house that night. We were used to the normal sounds — the expanding and contracting of heat pipes, the hum of the refrigerator as the motor kicked on, even the creaking of the floorboards that were more than a hundred and fifty years old. Never had we heard knocks on the wall, or the strange ticking sounds which immediately followed, then suddenly ceased.

The fourth night we woke from our sleep startled. There was a tremendous banging, a thunderous quaking we felt sure would rattle the plaster walls once written on by imprisoned Confederate soldiers during the Civil War. As suddenly as it started it stopped. A momentary silence . . . then the slow, steady *tick tick tick* which always followed.

We bolted to our feet, determined to find the source and direction of the sounds. We moved into the hallway and listened intently. The living room?

Stepping over the threshold and flicking on the light-switch inside the door, there was a sudden and instant recognition: the metronome! The device sat on the piano ticking as if keeping time to some unseen orchestra, even though it had not been used for years; and next to it the little man was askew. Even then from its cockeyed angle it seemed to stare at us, unblinkingly.

The strange sounds were not heard again until some time later, when we had gathered in the living room one evening to chat. There was a noise from downstairs — a creaking sound, as if the back door was opening. We stopped talking and crept down the stairs to investigate. The old wooden door was open, motionless in the still night; nothing was seen down the three flights of stairs which led to the backyard so infamous in the annals of history*, not even by the bright moonlight. The door was closed and secured with bolt and chain, then we returned upstairs to resume the conversation.

It wasn't long afterward we heard another sound, one very similar to the first. Hushed, we rose and started making our way down the stairs, determined to expose whatever intruder might lurk in the halls filled with wall writings.

There was no one. Only the back door, now unbolted and unchained, creaked on its rusty hinges as though buffeted by currents of air. The air was still.

The next event was eerier still. We came home one afternoon and entered the living room to find the pewter candlesticks made by the town pewtersmith on the floor, ten feet from the shelving where they normally sat. Nothing else appeared disturbed. We walked to the candlesticks and started to pick them up, then froze aghast. As though giant hands had taken them in a vicelike grip, the candlesticks had been crushed, the form of the fingers clearly indented into the hard metal. Both were gouged and scratched as

---

* During John Brown's raid in 1859, it is told angry townspeople captured one of the raiders and led him down "Hog Alley" to the backyard of this house. Chained to a post then stabbed with rusty knives, the raider was allowed to be eaten by the hungry hogs.

though an extremely hard object had been raked repeatedly over the surface of the lovely pewter. There seemed to be no explanation.

Events continued to plague us. Paintings mysteriously fell to the floor, cords unbroken, nails intact. Foodstuffs somehow would be pulled out of kitchen cupboards and spilled on the floor. The wall knockings continued. And coming home one day we found an intricate and beautifully constructed letter *J* carefully etched on the inside of one old rippled pane of glass.

The mysteries of the house aroused our curiosity as well as our suspicions.

We understood now why some townspeople had tried to warn us the house was haunted when we moved in. We were sorry we hadn't inquired then into the legends which might accompany the house; but it wasn't long before we learned the story of Jacob and the fateful night in which he died.

Our neighbor told us the story known by other residents. Her great grandmother, living in the same house in 1863, was an eyewitness to the gruesome events that transpired one summer night.

During the war, when the house was used by Union soldiers as a prison, a guard named Jacob left his post one night to visit a girlfriend. While away, his superiors toured the town in a surprise inspection and found his post vacant. Although Jacob's friends tried to excuse his absence, the inspecting officers learned where Jacob was, and the friends were punished for trying to conceal the guard's whereabouts.

23

Jacob returned later, not knowing his absence had been detected. His friends were waiting for him.

To teach him not to get them in trouble again, they pulled him to the floor. Stuffing feathers in his ears, nose and mouth, they punched and poked at him as he squirmed in distress. After what they figured a suitable period of discomfort, they released the helpless guard and stood back to let him rise. But Jacob didn't move. He had suffocated.

The soldiers were panic-stricken at the thought of their friend's accidental death, and hastily decided to hide the body behind the house before sunrise.

They found some boards and nails and began constructing a large box in which to transport the body down the back stairs to the ground. They hoped in the event they were seen an observer would think records or books were being carried.

After much pounding the rudimentary coffin was at last finished, and the body was placed inside. They had started down the stairs with the bulky box when one soldier lost his footing. The coffin slid down the stairs and split open, spilling its contents on the ground for anyone to see.

Neighbors, awakened by the pounding hammers and noises in the middle of the night, curiously peered out their windows to see in the moonlight frantic soldiers scrambling to collect boards and move a lifeless body. The authorities were notified, the soldiers arrested, and the complete story was finally told of Jacob's unfortunate demise.

Jacob's body was buried at a plain, unadorned gravesite nearby. Some say the ground above the grave turns scarlet and strangely damp during certain times of the year. Others swear apparitions and flickering lights can be seen both in the house and near the gravesite. Few who have lived in the house will deny there is something peculiar within its ancient walls. No one has wanted to make it a home for long.

The Gray Lady

Route 671 begins near Harpers Ferry and winds through the rolling Virginia countryside to Hillsboro, past sprawling farms, historic churches, and graveyards filled with tombstones dating back long before the Civil War. It is a pleasant area in which to live, one rich in history and scenic beauty. Not long ago an old log house built in 1752 was sold, and a family from Washington, D.C. moved in — not knowing their prized purchase already contained occupants of a different sort.

The day school began in September was the first time they knew of the ghost. The children had climbed aboard the school bus and the husband had left for work when the woman heard the sounds. There was someone walking upstairs. She called, asking who was still in the house, but there was no answer. Putting her cup of coffee on the table, she walked to the staircase and peered up to the landing, but nothing was seen. Then she heard the sounds again — someone was on the second floor walking across a room, opening drawers. She bravely marched up the stairs, self-consciously stomping her feet on each step, to warn intruders she was coming, or perhaps to help ward off the creepy feeling she had of knowing someone was around the corner but knowing not whom.

She found no one upstairs. But the drawers were open and disheveled clothing lay about on the floor.

The woman called again but there was no answer. She went to the window and looked outside. There was no car in the driveway. She got the shotgun.

Then she heard it again — but this time the noises were coming from the third floor. Someone was in the house, and she was afraid to look further.

The second time it happened the house was full of people. Several friends had come over for supper, and all seven at the dinner table heard the sounds. Someone was in the attic walking around, opening drawers.

The boys left the table and went upstairs. Searching the attic thoroughly, they found nothing unusual. As they walked downstairs they stopped at the third floor landing startled. They heard someone walking, moving drawers . . . noises coming from the attic.

On one wintry day the woman had gone out to the barn. When she returned, at 11:30 A.M., she was surprised to see a fire blazing in the fireplace. Strange occurrences around the house continued, and one day the man and woman mentioned it to their neighbors.

"Oh yes," acknowledged the man living near them. "We know of the strange things going on in that house. My sister heard the noises 45 years ago. But I have no idea what causes it, or why."

On one occasion the family was having guests overnight. They had gone to bed early, hoping for a good night's rest.

At four A.M. the telephone rang. The woman stirred and started to get up to answer the phone in the kitchen, but the ringing stopped after three rings. Since she was up she decided to continue to the kitchen to get a glass of water.

The hallway from the bedroom was dark, but there was no mistaking what she saw as she came into the kitchen. Standing by the sink in the moonlight was a ghostly figure of a lady about five feet tall. She wore a long, flowing gray dress, and had her hair parted in the middle, with gray braids falling down her back. She was holding a glass of water.

"Here you are, my dear," the woman intoned in a voice surprisingly firm.

"Who . . . who are you?" the amazed woman asked. But the figure only smiled wanly and held out the glass of water, repeating her offer.

The woman took the glass and turned, then looked back over her shoulder. Whatever apparition she had seen had vanished. She returned to bed a bit shaken, not at all sure she had really seen the ghost or dreamed it.

The next morning the family and guests convened for breakfast.

"Gosh, you keep strange hours!" remarked one of the guests.

"What do you mean?" asked the woman.

"The phone woke us last night, and we heard you talking with someone in the kitchen. Who was the other person? We didn't recognize the voice."

She told them of her "dream" and of the glass of water. They went to her bedroom, and on the nightstand was a partially filled glass. They knew she had not been dreaming. It was only one more encounter with the ghost that continues to haunt the house in Virginia.

The Haunting Melody

Each year on Christmas morning one can walk down a street in Emmitsburg near the Catoctin Mountains and hear the strains of a distant haunting melody played by an unseen flutist.

The musician's name is Larry Dielman. He died many years ago.

Larry's father, Dr. Henry Casper Dielman, came to America from Germany where he was a respected composer and musician. He was hired to teach music at Mount St. Mary's College in Emmitsburg, Maryland. It was the father's desire that his son become a musician also, and Larry became an accomplished flutist, practicing with his father and writing new arrangements, particularly for holiday hymns.

Christmas at the Dielman home was unique. After the usual exchange of presents, relatives and guests gathered round to hear Larry and his father present their duet compositions and arrangements specially prepared for this event. Their mastery of the flute was well known in the area. The concert became synonymous with "the Dielman Christmas," and townsfolk came to share in the beautiful music and hymn singing as an annual event.

Then one autumn Larry's father died. Only the memory of the enchanting Christmas mornings remained. The next Christmas Larry rose early, and wrapping his flute in the soft lined pouch handed down to him, walked sadly up the steep hill to the cemetery.

Kneeling by his father's grave, he unwrapped his flute and began playing. In the crisp early morning air the music seemed to float down the hill to the town, and to the residents the haunting melodies assumed an almost unworldly quality.

Many families hearing the music donned their coats and climbed the hill to the ridge where Larry knelt. Joining hands, they softly sang as Larry played his father's favorite Christmas hymn, "With Glory Lit the Midnight Air." It was a beautiful experience, and Larry's pilgramage with his flute to the cemetery on Christmas mornings became an annual event with area residents for years.

But one Christmas morning the flute was silent. Residents climbed the steep hill to the burial site and found Larry sitting under a tree, too ill to play. He was helped down the hill to his home, where he died several days later of pneumonia.

Christmas mornings in the town are quiet now. But after the initial excitement of gift opening has waned, some residents stand outside on their doorsteps, listening. Haunting in its quality yet clear and distinct in the morning air, the lonely voice of a flute is heard drifting over the snow-capped trees to the town below. Moments later it fades . . . until another year.

The Battle at Midnight

"What in heaven's name is *that*?" gasped the sleepless man on the observatory at the top of South Mountain House. Alone at the late hour, none of the other guests staying for the evening were awake to answer his self-directed question.

He stood for several moments, looking toward the east. In the field below thin wisps of smoke curled through the limbs of several trees, very near the barn that he had toured that day with the other guests. Fearing fire, the man went downstairs to wake a gentleman he had met only that day, but with whom he seemed to share common interests.

They hurriedly climbed to the observatory together. In the bright moonlight the smoke was clearly visible, and both remarked that they smelled the strong odor of sulphur. The wisps of smoke were rising at a more rapid rate near the trees, and strangely, several other clouds of gray smoke seemed to be rising in the open field. They decided to wake Henry, the servant, at once.

Henry didn't have to be wakened. Sitting in his room in a chair propped precariously on the wall, he was just finishing a bottle of whiskey when the two entered. Embarrassed at having been discovered imbibing, he sat upright and tried to put the bottle on the floor out of sight, but the bottle toppled over, spilling the small remainder of liquid on the floor.

"Henry, come at once! There seems to be a fire near the barn! Do you think we should call the others?" asked one of the gentlemen.

Henry rose, trying to collect himself. He would surely find himself in trouble if the household were awakened.

"No," he said, taking a deep breath. "I shall investigate."

The two men looked at one another questioningly, then handed Henry a torch. They walked down the hallway to the porch door, where Henry asked again where the fire was supposed to be.

"We think it is near the barn. Shall we come with you?" suggested the man. Henry shook his head and started down the path, while the disturbed men went to wait on the veranda.

Twenty minutes later Henry returned. He said he had gone beyond the barn, which he had examined, and proceeded as far as the gardener's house — and all was still and safe. Then he shuffled off to bed, mumbling that he had been bothered for "nothing at all."

Surprised and more puzzled than ever, the two watchers returned to the observatory.

The moon was brighter than usual, and the atmosphere seemed charged. Looking down at the fields that once had been the stage for one of the most bloody and hard-fought battles of the Civil War, the two witnessed a scene never to be forgotten.

The circlets of smoke took on a vaporous glamour, but yet defined as if opaque. Moments later they formed an image so disconcerting to the educated gentlemen they stood trembling in the midnight air.

The sharp smell of sulphur permeated the air. Shrouded wraiths formed above the ground and moved across the moonlit sky. Marshalling into approaching columns, phantom-like soldiers began converging as if ready to battle. At the moment of collision there was a shattering clash of sabers and an explosion so loud as to shake the house.

Lamps were lighted and people stirred. What had caused the terrible commotion? The ensuing investigation revealed nothing but the two guests still on the observatory, speechless and trembling, feebly pointing toward an empty field.

Fifty years later the warring phantoms were again seen in the field below South Mountain House. Two hikers of the Appalachian Trail had stopped for the evening, and after setting up camp, quickly fell asleep. About 11:00 they bolted upright, shedding their sleeping bags. The sound of clashing metal had startled them awake. Particularly alarming was the proximity of the sound, originating perhaps a hundred yards from where they were camped.

They were noting the curious odor in the air when the scene was unveiled before their unsuspecting eyes.

Across the field luminescent spirits danced above the ground, clad in the garb of soldiers. A chilly wind blew in the faces of the hikers as the phantom soldiers silently moved into position. There was another sound of clashing sabers and a dull explosion, and the spectres started across the horizon. Minutes later the phantoms vanished as suddenly as they had appeared, leaving the frightened adventurers with recurring nightmares of the ghost-ridden field on South Mountain.

The Snarly Yow

Around the turn of the century, a beast resembling a huge dog with large paws and an ugly red mouth was known to exist on South Mountain, east of Hagerstown, Maryland. Hundreds of people saw the dog, and horses particularly were afraid of the strange animal. The dog suddenly would appear on the National Pike, now Alternate Route 40, blocking the road. Without inflicting any damage with its vicious-looking teeth, it would confront travellers, then disappear before astonished men and women. The Black Dog, or Snarly Yow, as the locals called it, seemed to have been relegated to old accounts and memoirs . . . until the beast was again seen by credible witnesses in the summer of 1975.

Some time ago, William, a strong and sober man of 30, was returning home to his family the night he encountered the Snarly Yow. He had accomplished his errands in Boonsboro and was approaching the South Mountain section called Glendale when he saw the animal.

Under the bright stars the ungainly form of the beast could be distinctly traced. It was black, much bigger than any dog he had ever seen. As he came nearer, the animal moved to the center of the National Pike, blocking his way.

William first tried to scare the dog, then threw sticks and rocks at it. But instead of striking the creature, the objects seemed to go *through* the animal, having no effect whatsoever. The dog glared at him and threateningly bared its wolfish teeth in a snarl. Without making a sound the beast turned, then continued across the road into a thicket.

Another man, known to area residents as one of the best marksmen in the region, also came upon the Snarly Yow on the National Pike. Taking aim with his rifle, he fired several well-directed shots at the animal, but each speeding bullet passed through the shadowy beast, leaving no mark. The huntsman fled terrified.

A mountain man, nicknamed "Big Joe" due to his stature, came across the Black Dog on horseback one day while riding on a trail. The dog started running before the horse, and he gave chase. The dog kicked up dirt and gravel, very much as any beast with claws would do in a rapid run — then suddenly vanished.

Another man had gone to Boonsboro for an evening of entertainment. He became so rowdy and noisy an attempt was made to arrest him, but he successfully outwitted his assailants, mounted his horse and started home. Coming across the dog he tried to spur his horse on, but the horse became so terrified it threw the man to the ground, breaking his collar-bone in the fall. The dog vanished.

Others have thrown bricks and stones at the dog, only to have it walk away undaunted.

An itinerant minister, returning along the road after holding evening prayer in the little whitewashed church near

Glendale, claimed to have seen the dog on several occasions.

No one knows the origin of the Black Dog that supposedly lives in the woods of South Mountain, but even after more than seventy years of existence it was reported by a carload of people who had visited Washington Monument and were returning to Middletown. Approaching a ridge on the mountain, they saw a black dog suddenly before them. There was no avoiding the animal, and they felt the dull thud of the animal as it was crushed under the wheels of the car. They stopped, but to their surprise saw fifty feet behind them the huge black dog with clumsy paws standing on the road, glaring at them. The dog bared its teeth as if in defiance, then without a sound vanished before their eyes.

The Phantom Army

The two sisters had prepared to go to bed early the night the phantom army marched down Ridge Street in Harpers Ferry. The lights had been turned off in the upstairs bedrooms when one sister heard the sounds.

It was a quiet sound at first, then louder — a steady beat, seemingly getting nearer. She called to her sister: had a radio been left on? The response was negative, and she settled down to go to sleep, thinking the sound must be the hot water pipes in the walls.

But the steady beat continued, louder by the moment. Then she realized it was the first Saturday in June and the heat was not on; she could think of no explanation for the mysterious sounds. She lay listening to the sound intently, wide awake, and gradually realized the approaching sounds were drum rolls. She got out of bed and went to the window to see what was transpiring so late at night, but there was nothing unusual to be seen on the moonlit street. When she went back to bed the drum rolls suddenly ceased.

About two blocks from where the sisters live, another woman was reading a book in her house on a Saturday afternoon while waiting for her husband to return from work.

She too heard the sound of approaching drums in the distance, but being in a town frequented by tourists, thought nothing particularly unusual by the promise of a parade or perhaps the high school band practicing. She put down her book and went to the front door, which faced the main street of Harpers Ferry, to view the source of the music. But there was nothing unusual on this summer day; the steady traffic in and out of town was quite normal.

The sound of the drum rolls grew louder. Curious, she opened the door and went to the edge of the road. Looking in the direction of Camp Hill, she saw no one. Still the music was coming nearer.

Perplexed, she realized that despite the approaching sounds there was going to be no parade. The source of the music soon passed by her: drums rolling, men whispering to one another, the sound of the boots marching on the pavement, then fading as the invisible procession made its way down the hill.

These and many other residents and tourists have heard the phantom army and drum corps during the last five years, but numerous reportings of these strange phenomena date back more than a century and a half.

In 1799, troops under the command of General Pinkney were sent to Harpers Ferry in anticipation of a war with France. Troops were quartered on a ridge near Harper's Cemetery, afterwards known as Camp Hill. As diplomatic negotiations took a considerable while in those days, there wasn't a great deal for the troops to do. They filled their days by marching up and down the streets to the accompaniment of a drum corps.

When the threat of war passed, many of the troops settled in the town. An epidemic of cholera followed, killing many in the area. For years after, residents refused to live either around Harper's Cemetery or Camp Hill, claiming it haunted. Many reported hearing ghostly drum rolls and men whispering, although nothing was ever seen.

Eventually, as new settlers moved into the area, there was less anxiety about populating the areas adjacent to the two haunted sites. The phantom army continued to march through the years, however, recurringly astonishing even the most steadfast non-believers.

Fiery Mansion

Nestled along a deserted country lane not far from the Potomac River in Shepherdstown, West Virginia, is Fiery Mansion. Townspeople claim it is haunted.

Now a run down old building, it used to be the fine home of Dr. Fiery, a Shepherdstown dentist. According to the story told by townspeople who know the house and the events that led to its state of disrepair, the doctor's wife was paralyzed from her hips down, and was forced to spend much of her time in a wheelchair.

One summer evening Dr. Fiery left his home and went to his office. He had left his wife upstairs in her bedroom, brushing her hair. Upon returning, he found his wife crumpled at the bottom of the stairs, her wheelchair on top of her lifeless body. Her once dark hair was ashen white; apparently something had frightened her to death. Whatever she had seen must have been witnessed by Dr. Fiery also, for he ran from the house never to be heard of again.

Many area residents approach the house with caution.

"You can believe what you want to believe," said one resident of the town. "But there is something to that place."

The person tells of going to the house one night with several friends. They claim to have heard "the loudest blood-curdling scream" behind them, followed seconds later by a scream down the lane, then seconds later another scream was heard in the house.

"It was the most frightening thing that has ever happened to me," the resident says.

On another occasion, a man had gone through the house without noticing anything strange. He came out of the house and started to get into his car when he heard a rumbling sound, as if the house was caving in. But when he looked back the house was standing intact, eerily quiet. Several witnesses confirmed the story.

Other residents claim to have had similar experiences.

A man and his wife went to the house one afternoon out of curiosity. Parking their car in the lane, they had started toward the house when they saw a shadowy figure of a woman in a long dress standing at the window. The wraith-like woman seemed to fade, then disappeared altogether.

The house was recently purchased, but no one as yet has been willing to live there. Neighbors insist it is haunted, and one man insists he saw the fearsome figure who restlessly roams the place many years after the tragic events occurred.

The Phantom Coach of Carter Hall

Carter Hall, eleven miles from Winchester, Virginia, near the village of Millwood, was built by the Burwell family in 1792. After building stately homes in Tidewater Virginia, the Burwells built Carter Hall as a summer home. Each year the family would arrive by great lumbering coaches, loaded with children, baggage and servants. They usually departed for their permanent home in the autumn, but becoming especially fond of the area, eventually made this mansion their home year round.

The Burwells entertained a great deal, and members of the new government of the United States made Carter Hall a favorite rest stop. Edmund Randolph, first Secretary of State, died in the house while on a visit to Colonel Nathaniel Burwell. He is buried in the graveyard of the Old Chapel nearby. Whether it is his ghost, other dignitaries, or that of the Burwell family, no one is quite sure. But people say Carter Hall is haunted.

It was on a moonlit night in springtime many years ago the family living in Carter Hall heard the phantom coach. They were in the parlor entertaining guests, playing cards, laughing and joking. They paused at the sound of noises in the driveway. They heard the jingle of harness and horses' feet stamping.

"Listen!" someone said. "Must be company coming!"

Several people hastened to the front door. Outside the moonlight bathed the drive in front of the tall white columns. The lawn sloped away to the oak woods where the Indians used to hold their dances. Further off the Blue Ridge Mountains traced their shadowy outline against the sky. All was quiet and serene. No one was there.

The family returned to the parlor to continue the conversation, and one sat down at the harpsichord to play. Then they heard it again.

A carriage was coming up the driveway to the front of the house. They distinctly heard the coachman's whip cracking. The carriage stopped and a door slammed. Then with a heavy rumble the carriage drove away, crunching gravel under the wheels. No one knocked at the door.

A silence fell over the people gathered in the room.

"It was the coach," someone whispered.

Once more the phantom coach of Carter Hall was heard.

Wizard Clip

On a stormy and windswept night in 1794 a stranger
rode up on horseback to the farmhouse of Adam Livingston,
a sober and industrious farmer living in Middleway, Virginia.
The stranger was middle-aged and well dressed, and asked
for lodging in Livingston's home for the night or until the
weather cleared. Livingston consulted his wife and seven
children and accepted the man, not knowing this night was
to be the beginning of years of torment and distress, eventually resulting in the infamous story of Wizard Clip.

As was the custom, Livingston and the stranger talked
before retiring for the evening. The stranger reported he was
only passing through the area, as he was on business in another city. He thanked Livingston for his hospitality, then
went to his room to go to bed.

In the middle of the night Livingston woke hearing the
man wheezing and coughing. He went to the stranger's door
and asked if he was all right. The man asked Livingston to
come to his side, which he did, and whispered that he was
very ill, and was afraid he might die. He told Livingston of
the sins he committed during his life, and regretted that as a
Roman Catholic he had not confessed his sins earlier and

been absolved. He then asked Livingston if a Catholic priest was nearby, and pleaded for his host to get one right away.

Livingston left the room and woke his wife. Devout Lutherans, they felt antagonistic toward the Catholic church, and after hearing her husband's story, the wife swore no Catholic priest was ever going to enter their house. She bade him to forget the request, especially on such a stormy night, and return to bed. Livingston listened to his wife, and not knowing where a priest could be found anyway, went back to sleep.

The next morning the guest did not appear for breakfast and Livingston, a good deal alarmed, went to the stranger's room and found him dead. A few neighbors were notified, and they helped commit the unknown man to a nameless grave.

Returning from the funeral late in the evening, the family built a fire in the fireplace and settled around it, discussing the occurrences of the previous night. Suddenly the fire flared, and several blazing logs leaped from the fireplace and whirled around the floor in a weird dance, sputtering sparks over the hand-made rug and floor.

Livingston and his family jumped from their seats and raced about the room, trying to extinguish the fiery logs, but no sooner had they trapped a log and returned it to the fireplace it sprang to the floor again to resume its seemingly possessed dance.

This continued throughout the night, and not a member of the family could rest, fearing for the safety of their house and their lives. Yet in the morning the fire quieted as suddenly as it had come to life the evening before, and the relieved family collapsed on their beds exhausted from the night's exertion.

The next night Livingston awoke disturbed to hear the sound of horses galloping around his house. He arose and looked out the window at the moonlit farm but saw nothing to assure him it was anything but a figment of his imagination. The sounds continued for an hour, then stopped. The shaken man returned to bed, only to spend a restless night.

Worn out, scared and disconsolate, Livingston next day walked down the road that passed by his house, and greeted a man driving a wagon. The man had stopped his team and looked angry. Livingston asked what was the problem, and the man gruffly replied Livingston knew well what the problem was — why had he stretched a rope across the road, impeding traffic?

Livingston saw no rope and wanted to know what the apparently drunken teamster meant by accusing him of such a ridiculous thing. The driver demanded the rope be removed at once, in order that he could continue. Not seeing Livingston make any effort to remove the obstruction, the driver cursed the farmer, got out of his wagon, drew a knife and slashed at the rope. But the knife merely passed through the air, cutting nothing. As the wagoner stared amazed, another wagon arrived, and again the driver wanted to know why the rope was across the road detaining him. Joining the other driver he too tried to cut the rope, but his knife met no resistance. Livingston then suggested they cautiously proceed down the road, ignoring the phantom rope. As they mounted their wagons and started, they were dumbstruck to see their horses and wagons drive *through* the rope, as though it didn't exist at all except before their eyes.

Soon, however, other teams arrived, and each cursed Livingston anew for the obstacle. Finding their teams also able to pass through the rope, the word spread quickly throughout the area there were some very strange things happening about the place.

A week after the stranger's burial, Livingston's barn burned and his cattle died. The crockery in his house, by no visible means, was thrown on the floor and broken. His money disappeared, and various animals on the farm were found mysteriously decapitated.

The demon, already having destroyed the peace, then assumed a new form. The sound of a large pair of shears could be distinctly heard in the house, clipping his blankets, sheets, boots, saddles and clothing in the shape of half-moons or crescents.

Word spread quickly about the new form of the demon, and people from a 30 mile radius came to hear or see a sign of the devil. One lady visitor was strolling with Mrs. Livingston one day, admiring her fine flock of ducks. Suddenly they heard a *snip snip* sound flying around their ears, and as they covered their hair, they saw, one by one, the head of each duck fall to the ground. Many other witnesses saw the same event.

An old lady from nearby Martinsburg, hearing of these strange events, went to Livingston's to satisfy her curiosity. Before entering she took her new black silk cap and carefully wrapped it in a handkerchief. She placed it in her pocket to spare it from being clipped. Awhile later she

stepped out of the house to go home, and as she unwrapped the handkerchief she found her cap cut into narrow ribbons.

There lived in Middleway a German tailor who thought the demon a stupid superstition, and openly boasted that not only would he stay in the house alone at night, but given enough time he would expose the true source of the wizard clipping. One day he was passing by the Livingston farm carrying a package containing a suit made for a nearby planter. *Clip Clip!* The tailor heard the shears about his head and told the maker of the sound to "go for damn." Arriving at his destination he proudly unwrapped his suit only to find the cloth full of crescent-shaped slits and utterly ruined. There are numerous stories of the havoc caused by the diabolical shears.

The continuing of the mysterious clipping — always repeated within a 24 hour period of time — aroused the country for miles around. Livingston's health began to fail visibly due to his great consternation and lack of sleep. He found several professed conjurers who offered to help, but their incantations were all in vain.

Shortly after this he had a dream. He thought he was climbing a high mountain, and had difficulty making the ascent. After considerable struggle he reached the top, where he found an imposing man dressed in robes. He then heard a voice say, "This is the man who can help you." His wife woke him at this point, as he was groaning, and he told her of the dream. Not knowing any minister who wore robes, he decided to inquire in the morning.

Livingston's inquiries eventually brought him to the home of the McSherry family, who were Roman Catholics. He had learned a priest often stopped to visit the family while passing through the area, and Livingston desperately clung to a hope the family could lead him to the man of his dream.

Knocking on the door, he asked to see "the priest." Mrs. McSherry, who answered the door, reported he wasn't there, but he was scheduled to deliver the service in a church in Shepherdstown the following Sunday. He thanked her and returned home, feeling much disappointed.

On the appointed day Livingston left his home and arrived at the church early. When the priest finally appeared at the altar, Livingston was overcome. Falling to his knees with tears streaming down his face, he exclaimed, "This is the very man I saw in my dream; he is the one the voice told me would relieve me from my troubles." When the service was over he told the priest his sad story. But the Rev. Dennis Cahill laughed and suggested it must be some of his neighbors playing pranks on him.

Others in the congregation, who had stayed after the service and knew of the demon at Livingston's home, corroborated his story. Father Cahill finally agreed to visit his home.

At the house, Father Cahill sprinkled holy water about, which had no effect whatsoever on the demon. He then left some money on the doorsill, where coins previously had been taken away. But this too had no effect, and the mysterious clipping continued.

Finally, Father Cahill decided to perform a mass in the home. Livingston grew excited, and remembering the stranger's request, employed the priest to perform the rites in the room where the traveller had died. Father Cahill consented, and no evidence of a demon was heard or seen again.

On February 21, 1802, feeling deeply indebted to the priest for relieving his misery, Livingston deeded to the Catholic church a 34 acre tract of land named "Priest's Field," now located just outside Middleway, West Virginia. On the property, a small stone cross still marks the grave of the unknown traveller.

The Slave House

In a little field by the side of present-day Route 340 near Charles Town, West Virginia, stood a small building once used as a house for slaves. After the Civil War the structure was abandoned, but travellers on foot used the building for overnight shelter. However, over the years the house acquired a reputation for being other than friendly; horrible apparitions were seen that sent the frightened itinerant occupants into the fields, running in terror.

Long ago, two brothers travelling the road stopped at the house to spend the evening. After supper each went to separate bedrooms and quickly fell asleep. Several hours later both were awakened with the strange feeling of not being alone.

Phosphorescent figures began materializing in the rooms of the house, at first dimly, then brighter. Initially the figures were indistinguishable. Then before their amazed eyes the images assumed a form so grisly in its appearance the men screamed.

Headless slaves tied to one another with a heavy chain oozed blood from their severed arteries. The figures seemed to glow, illuminating the rooms with a weird pulsating light.

The brothers dashed from their rooms terrified, brushing against the apparitions, and ran shrieking from the house. Hours later they were found quaking along the side of the road, mumbling unintelligibly, covered with blood.

The building burned in 1952, and the location is today marked only by a patch of lillies. Some nights people see a strange glow in the field where the house stood; others, remembering their experiences there, refuse to go near the place.

Death Curve

Alternate Route 40 curves sharply left, then right, at a place between Boonsboro and Funkstown, Maryland. It is a dangerous series of curves that has led to many accidents. People call it Death Curve.

During a winter many years ago, a man and his dog were returning home late one evening in his horse-drawn carriage. The winding road was slippery and icy, and at an angular turn the man lost control. The carriage skidded across the road into the embankment, throwing the driver to the ground. Frightened by the sound of splintering wood, the horse bolted, dragging the carriage laden with supplies over the man's neck. His head was severed from his body.

Other travellers came across the gory scene and removed the body. The head of the man was never found, nor was the dog. People say Death Curve is haunted.

On a foggy night in the autumn of 1950 a woman came out of her house to empty a bucket of water. She glanced over her shoulder and to her surprise saw a man dressed in a dark suit standing on the porch steps. She put the bucket down and started walking toward the man to ask him what he wanted, then froze. The man was headless. The woman saw the man climb to the second step of the porch, then disappear.

One night in 1965 a man and woman were driving along the old route to their home in Hagerstown. The driver slowed at the sharp bend and switched on the bright head-lights. They saw a man walking along the road with his back toward them. Illuminated by the carlights, the traveller on foot suddenly stopped and turned, revealing a decap-itated body. As the driver slammed on the brakes the figure vanished.

Two years ago a man was walking along the road near the curve and heard a dog run up beside him. He reached down to pat the dog, but nothing was felt or seen. Yet he distinctly heard the dog panting. He walked faster, and heard the dog also increase its pace; then the sound of the animal ceased as he rounded the curve.

Today, people who know these stories approach Death Curve with caution. It is fraught with the dangers of the unknown, and considered well named.

The Child in the Corner

In the town of Bolivar, adjacent to Harpers Ferry, there is a large old home that has been converted into an antique shop.

A woman was touring the house with the owner one day.

"Who is that child?" asked the visitor upon entering a room on the first floor. The lady was gazing intently at a small antique bed located in one corner of the room.

"What child? There is no child here."

The woman continued to gaze at the bed. She saw a small child, apparently very ill. Moments later the image began to fade, then disappeared altogether. She described at once everything she had seen, and the owner immediately went over to the bed, which seemed to him as usual, empty and undisturbed.

Several days later the owner met two elderly women who knew the house and of its former occupants, the McArthur family. The ladies remarked that Mrs. McArthur, a century ago, was the first woman offered a pension by the federal government for her service in the military.

Intrigued with the history of the house, he asked the ladies to continue.

They told him that Mr. McArthur, the local undertaker, operated his business in the two towns ravaged by war. He had a daughter who also lived here with her baby. But the child became ill and eventually died.

"Can you tell me which room the child died in?" he asked.

They named the location. It was the same room where the visitor two days earlier had seen the phantom child. He decided to move the bed to another area, and the child has not been seen again.

Prospect Hall

In the eighteenth century one of the most beautiful estates in Frederick County, Maryland, was Prospect Hall. Located outside of the City of Frederick, the home and grounds today are part of a private school, but the ghost of a former occupant is said to dwell within its venerable walls.

At one time, the family living at Prospect Hall had a son. At the age of 22 he was romantically inclined, and fell in love with the housekeeper, a mulatto slave.

The family strongly disapproved of the relationship and made plans to separate the two. The young man was put on a ship bound for England.

Shortly after the man left, the housekeeper mysteriously disappeared. It was rumored she had been locked in a closet, where she suffocated; others claimed she had been boarded up in the wall of the mansion.

Throughout the years various occupants of the house claim to have heard a muffled knocking on the walls, as though someone were trying to get out. Others have heard someone walking through the house, although upon investigation no one was found. When the house was vacant, some residents of the town say they saw a shadowy figure of a woman. They claim it is the ghost of the housekeeper roaming the house, futilely searching for her lost love.

The Blue Dog

Rose Hill Manor was built in the late eighteenth century by the son-in-law of the first governor of Maryland, Thomas Johnson. Located in the north section of Frederick, Maryland, the house is now owned by the county. It is reputed to be haunted by a ghostly blue dog that roams the grounds at midnight and then disappears.

Many years ago, long before banks became popular, a wealthy man lived at Rose Hill Manor with his dog. Before dying he buried his money somewhere on the estate. Although he left in his will instructions for finding the money ("six feet from the old oak tree"), no one was able to locate the buried treasure. Even now fortune hunters search for the man's gold, but all efforts have failed.

Area residents say sometimes they see a ghostly blue dog on the premises, and it is believed if one follows the dog one will be led to the gold. No one has been successful in following the phantom animal.

A ceramic plate was made recently depicting the figure of the dog. After it was put on display, the plate disappeared. Later it was found on the grounds of the estate, but no one could explain how or why it was removed from its original location. The plate was put back on display, then once more disappeared.

The mysterious occurrences at Rose Hill Manor are intriguing to some and alluring to others. Some anxiously await the day the dog can be followed to the buried gold.

The Grave

On July 1, 1975, something very strange happened in a cemetery west of Hagerstown, Maryland. Although extensive investigations were conducted, no explanation for the occurrence was found.

The aging caretaker of the cemetery noticed it at daybreak. The grass sod had been pushed up about eight inches, leaving a gaping hole beneath. He probed the hole with a flashlight and discovered it led down to a concrete vault whose lid was dislodged and broken.

The caretaker phoned the secretary-treasurer of the cemetery and told her what had happened. She immediately called the police and reported that a grave had been vandalized.

An officer arrived at the cemetery minutes later and investigated the grave for signs of tampering, such as shovel marks. He concluded the sod had apparently been thrust upward from the inside, without any human perpetration. He had no idea what caused it.

The secretary went back to her phone and called the

gas company. They dispatched a veteran employee to probe the area for methane and sewer gas which may have collected in an underground cavity and exploded. The search revealed nothing.

A funeral director arrived at the cemetery and suggested that the gas from the decaying body inside the vault somehow caused the eruption.

However, the marker which lay a few feet away said that the occupant was a three-year-old boy who had died in 1912. Not only would his body be small, but long past the gaseous stages of decay.

They decided the body would have to be exhumed in order to install a new vault. The diggers took only a short time to bring out the vault and casket. The seams of the vault, as well as its lid, were all broken, and the diggers brought it out of the grave in seven pieces.

The wooden casket was intact when they laid it on the grass. The cloth covering was rotting, but there were no signs of mildew.

Perhaps the answer to the eruption lay inside the small casket. The caretaker unlatched the lid, stood back, and opened it with his shovel.

The sun glared down on a child with long, blond hair that glowed in the first light of 63 years.

A light mold had collected on his face, dehydration had tightened the skin around the skull, and his once pink shroud was now beige, but otherwise, in the words of the caretaker, "He was as perfect as the day they put him there."

On his chest were a flower stem and a metal piece that said "Our Darling." At his feet was a small teddy bear.

By the middle of the afternoon the vault company had replaced the old broken vault with a new one. The well-preserved body of the small child was again buried; but he left a mystery behind him that no one has been able to answer.

How, or why, did his grave open by itself? What caused a concrete vault to erupt and push up several square feet of dirt? There were no lightning marks on the grave. Vandalism, natural gas and body gas had already been ruled out. No rational explanation could be offered.

The grave has been undisturbed ever since the strange occurrence in 1975.